WHAT ABOUT ME?

ALSO BY EDWARD KOREN

▼▼▼▼▼

Caution: Small Ensembles
Well, There's Your Problem
Are You Happy?
Do You Want to Talk About It?

WHAT ABOUT ME?

Cartoons from the New Yorker by Edward Koren

With a Preface by Calvin Trillin

PANTHEON BOOKS NEW YORK

TO THE MEMORY OF PAUL ZWEIG

AND TO ALL MY FRIENDS—WHO ARE IN THIS BOOK

 Published in the United States by Pantheon Books, a division of Random House, Inc., New York, and simultaneously in Canada by Random House of Canada Limited, Toronto.

Library of Congress Cataloging-in-Publication Data
Koren, Edward.
What about me?: New Yorker cartoons/by Edward Koren.
p. cm.
ISBN 0-679-72549-0
1. American wit and humor, Pictorial. 2. New Yorker (New York, N.Y.: 1925) I. Title.
NC1429.K62A4 1989
741.5'973—dc20 *89-42679*

Manufactured in the United States of America
Book Design by Fearn Cutler
First Edition

In a preface to Ed Koren's first book of cartoons, I reported that the question I had been asked most about him was whether he could draw a non-shaggy person or a beast of some identifiable species if he really tried. I also reported my answer: As far as I know, he's trying as hard as he can.

Thirteen years have passed, and Koren is still trying. It's perfectly obvious that he has made no progress whatsoever. In fact, his style is now so firmly established in the culture that people refer casually to a "Koren person" or a "Koren animal." At this point, if he did manage to draw, say, a conventional man walking an obvious Airedale, the drawing would undoubtedly be denounced as a fake, so he might as well give up.

For all of these years, I've been feeding Koren ideas. I just wish he'd take one of them. I've tried to adapt my ideas to his style. I don't just say, "See, there's this guy on a desert island . . ." I say, "See, there's this shaggy guy on a desert island . . ." I often present my ideas with introductions that echo Koren's reviews: "Say, if you're looking for a foible of middle-class contemporary American life to skewer with your keen eye and your uniquely expressive line . . ." No go.

In other words, this is sort of a reverse acknowledgment to say that I am not responsible for anything in this book. If you have any problems—if you come across a skewered foible that you hadn't realized was a foible, if you recognize yourself behind that shag—blame the author. If you think you recognize an Airedale, ask for your money back.

Calvin Trillin

"Call it vanity, call it narcissism, call it egomania. I love you."

"This past summer, I got deeply depressed about our planet—as if I didn't have enough problems of my own."

"Great tights!"

"The word you're searching for is 'wife.' "

"In this city, Jack, you learn to respect the pedestrian."

"You are about to experience something rare in your life, Stan—rejection."

MEN
DRINKING
COFFEE
CURTIS
SASHA
KOREN

"*Now* what?"

"I never get what I want."

"From a man's point of view, do you think it's beautiful?"

"And on my right is Joe Nast, representing an opposing viewpoint."

"My goodness, it's little Benjie! You've grown into quite a distinguished man!"

"Do you have the key?"

"Why not take her out for a spin? It'll blow your socks off!"

"Daddy has to clear his head for a few minutes before he can deal with 'Babar.'"

"O.K., *let's confront the issues of masculinity!*"

"New specs?"

"It looks like the ornithosuchians are attempting a comeback."

"This is Amanda, everybody—of David and Amanda."

"He's not one of my favorites."

"The weather looks a little iffy."

"I need a hug."

"I <u>knew</u> you were having an affair with your car!"

"How are her scores?"

"Do you think people had a nice time?"

"*Great set of pipes!*"

"As for me, I'm in various stages of deterioration."

"If you were to boil your book down to a few words, what would be its message?"

"Call off the siege. It's being converted into ninety-three units of cooperative housing."

"AAAAALLLLL RIIIGHT!"

"Reassess our life style? Why?"

"I was just thinking about you!"

"He's never accepted his divorce."

"Timothy, success is nothing to fear."

"Charles has offered his personal image for us to project as our corporate image."

"There's something you should consider before you begin—my hair works hard and it plays hard."

"We need a token man, and I guess you're it."

"It sure is great to have you back for a while at the mother ship."

KOREN

LATE FORTIES... MAYBE FIFTY... POSSIBLY A STILL VIGOROUS FIFTY-FIVE.

MID TO LATE THIRTIES... PERHAPS FORTY... AT MOST, A WELL-PRESERVED FORTY-TWO.
KOREN

"He's my escort, and he's a teddy bear."

"You may not recognize Bobby. He's turned into his father."

"Milt, I'm beginning to think that your illness is a disharmony of life energy."

I'M A LITTLE
OUT OF SORTS
TODAY
18
287
KOREN

"Nicholas, I want to thank you for sharing."

"I never get sick."

"Tonight, you're dessert!"

"My work is to stare into space."

"Is there someone here who is sensitive to the banking needs of women?"

"Mom, can me and Nat go down to the corner store and get some gelato?"

"The conversation has turned to parking."

"It was obviously built when the Mayans were feeling good about themselves."

"Well, there's mid-life."

"You have beautiful paws."

"I guess it's last night's second helping of German chocolate cake."

"Have a safe trip!"

"I love this place—its food, its ambience, and its political goals."

THESE PREMISES
PROTECTED BY
SELF-INTEREST
KOREN

"We hate to shop."

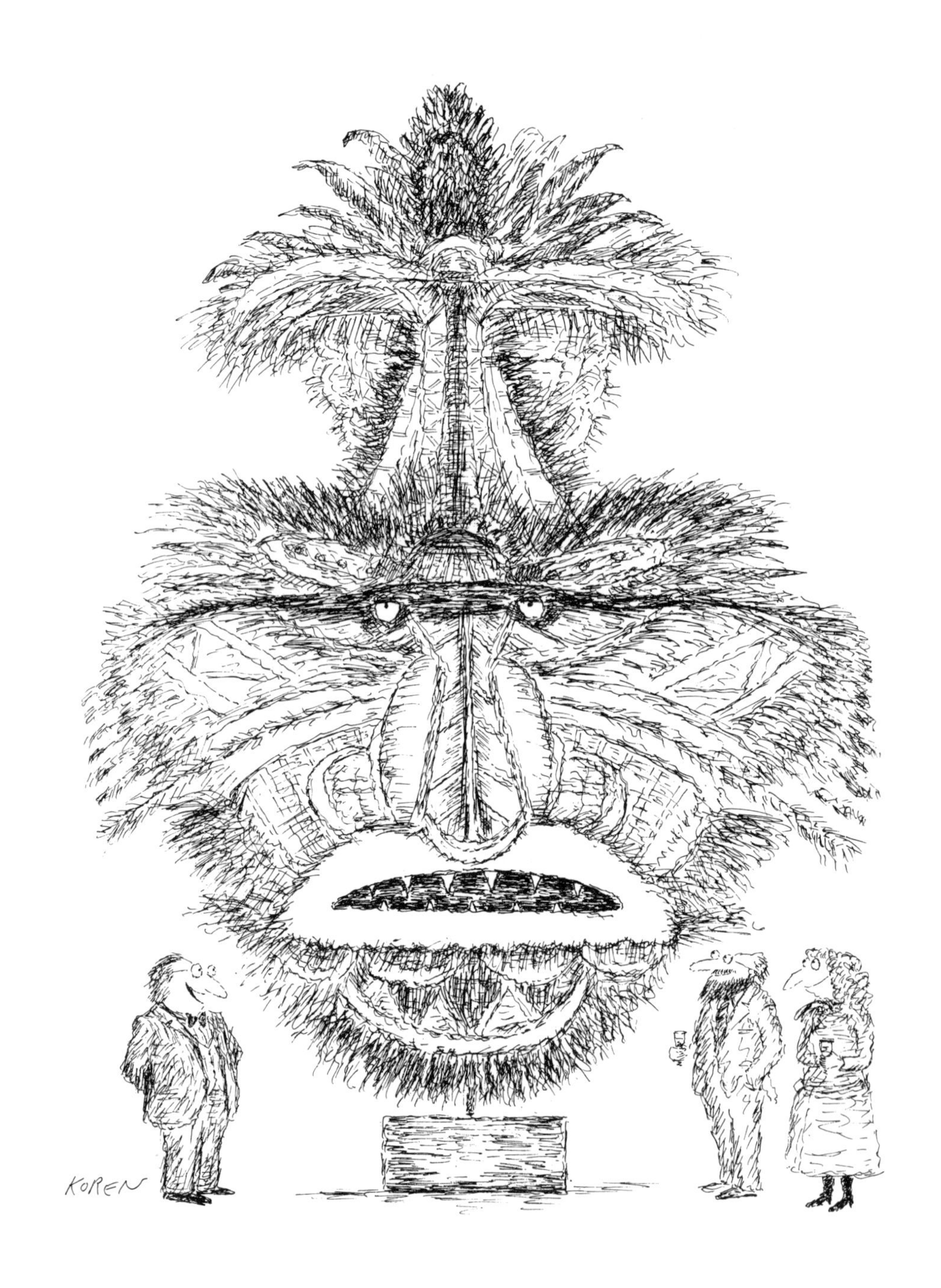

"Its mere possession is immensely satisfying."

"Sam, neither your father nor I consider your response appropriate."

"I hope you don't mind—I've brought my own yogurt."

"Do I detect a new resentment?"

"We're presenting this year's award to the tomato—for the way he has deepened our understanding of world-conflict resolution, for fostering the ideals of peace, friendship, and international brotherhood, and for being delicious."

"Your friend Andy thinks I'm sexy."

"I finally got too old for bluejeans."

"I know it's hard to believe, but this is a great Beaujolais town."

"Aren't you heartened by the return of elegance and good manners?"

"When I ask questions, I expect answers!"

"I despise my life, but I'm in love with my life style."

"Is your injury sports-related?"

"Could you repeat what you just said? I was on another planet."

"He's been mentioned as a possible husband."

"Catherine, we agreed—you would put on your mittens when your hands got cold."

"Quick, Jonathan—a local craftsperson."

"You'd make a formidable enemy."

"I'm a fancier of dogs and interesting men."

"Our group shares a lot of giggles."

"Would you prefer the talking or the non-talking section?"

"Our goal is to modernize it but retain the historical flavor."

"Hemingway! Is he any good?"

"After all their years together, Jonathan still tends to shy away from confrontation."

" 'Good' is not good enough."

"I'm in the mood for meat."

"Let's flee!"

"I heard you had a little problem with the law."

"Did you do the marathon?"

"My Mom says to come in and have a seat. She's on two lines and has three people on hold."

"Matthew, I'm having a lot of trouble with what you've just said."

"Something you should bear in mind, James. Sam has recently come into a lot of money."

"It's been real fun for all the crew
to take you through the sky.
Recall the super trip we had
next time you need to fly."

"I thought I'd give Western medicine one more chance."

TURBO

"I'm afraid California just isn't me."

"Kate, this is the wonderful new man I told you about who has such a strong hand with garlic and fresh thyme."

"Oh, sweetie, I'm sorry. I've been coming on like gangbusters again."

"No, you're not too late. Cathy's just beginning to put calcium into perspective."

"We've been admiring your fathering techniques."

"I'm afraid the antipasto is a bit rebellious this evening."

"I envy your talent—I never had much luck with cactus."

"Hey, you guys, don't you remember? The big word here is 'compromise.' "

SOON
TO BE
A
SWEATER

"I know you want me to be someone else—but someone else is not me!"

"Where's the business end of this thing?"

TEMPORARILY
CLOSED
TO
RETHINK
OUR
CONCEPT
KOREN

"Is the chef's salad better balanced nutritionally than the salade aux trois légumes?"

"Oh dear, I'm terrible with names."

"She's very driven."

"I hear you enjoy tinkering."

"Ah—*the celestial Mozart!*"

"I won't be home for dinner, dear. I'm stuck late at the office."

"Larry never gains an ounce!"

"Noah, I'm tired of doing battle with you!"

"Stab is with us tonight to try very hard to say something coherent about his new album."

"Frankly, I don't like women."

"Thanks, Dick. I needed someone to take me down a peg."

"We're here to experience pleasure."

"If you promise to be very careful, Mommy will let you carry the baguettes."

"The fish is on the top shelf of the fridge. The beans are in the blue pot. The salad greens are already washed and in the plastic bag and if you want to wait, Daddy will make a yummy dessert when he gets home."

"I love this planet!"

"Thank you. We laughed more in one night than we have in the last three years."

"And, finally, to my wife, my love and appreciation for her understanding and critical insights, without whom this project would never have been accomplished."